THIS BOOK BELONGS TO:

....

....

DADDY'S PEARL JAHI

Written by:
Subrena Joseph

Illustrated by:
Almasi Samuels

Tahitian, Tahi for short
was her Daddy's precious
little girl.
So precious he called her
'Daddy's Pearl'.

Tahi was fun loving,
adventurous, always smiling
and laughing with others.

Tahi had rich chocolate coloured
skin, in the right light you could
see a rainbow, shining through it

Her hair was like wool, and she wore short beaut
'locs' that were perfect for wearing beads.

Tahi's mummy always bought
lots, of different,
kinds of beads.

She loved wearing beads and flicking her head back and forth

Sometimes, when she did this, the beads would hit her head and even, her eyes

But Tahi's favourite
thing to do, or time of
the day, was when she
sat and talked with
Daddy.

She felt so grown up !

Tahi and Daddy would talk about

LOTS OF THINGS

and Daddy would answer

ALL

her questions.

This made her
feel so special.

Daddy would ask Tahi,
how she felt,
What Made Her Happy ?

.

What She Was Worried About ?
and what made her laugh

Tahi loved telling Daddy
what made her laugh

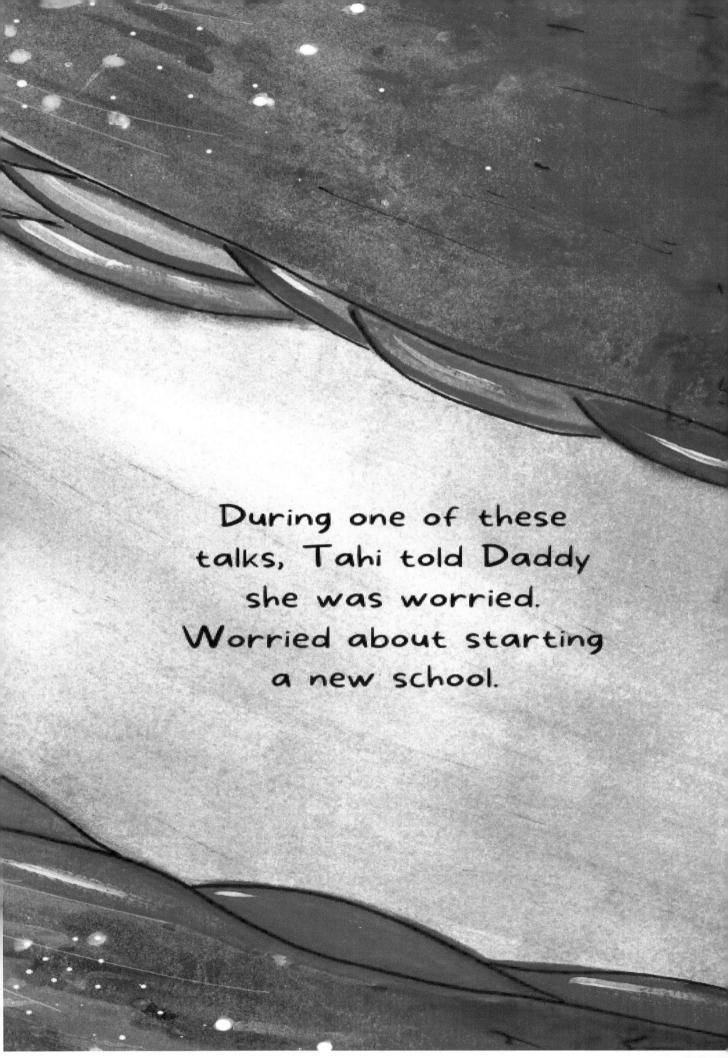

During one of these
talks, Tahi told Daddy
she was worried.
Worried about starting
a new school.

"Will they like me?"

"Will I make friends
Daddy?" she asked.

Daddy couldn't imagine Tahi ' his
Pearl' not making friends. Or people
not loving her, like he does, for her
smile, or being so unique.

So he hugged her and said "Yes, you will, make friends". He just knew her first day at school would be great.

Tahi first day at school she wore her brand new uniform. A pretty dress, white socks and shiny shoes. With matching beads in her hair

The started out good ,
Tahi was excited and smiling.

But that smile was gone,
at the end of the school day
Tahi had introduced herself, to some of
the girls, as Daddy's Pearl.

Something she had always been proud of !

When Daddy picked her up from school,
she ran to him crying

Daddy, she said
"They had beads in their hair like me"

"But they laughed and made fun of me"
she said through tears

Tahi's words were a little jumbled,
but she appeared to be saying
something about
Diamonds and Pearls.

When I said, "I'm Daddy's Pearl" .
They all said, they
"We are Daddy's Diamonds"
and giggled.

"They said, Diamonds are better
than Pearls "Tahi told Daddy.

Tahi looked into her Daddy's eyes
and said "Daddy, why am I a Pearl?

"Can I be Daddy's Diamond instead?"

To this Daddy responded with his own
sad eyes, "but Tahi, you are my Pearl ".

Daddy continued to wipe Tahi's tears
and asked, "Do you know how we get
to see a diamonds beauty?"

With curious eyes, Tahi shook her head.

Daddy explained, that both Diamonds
and Pearls are beautiful,
precious, and rare.

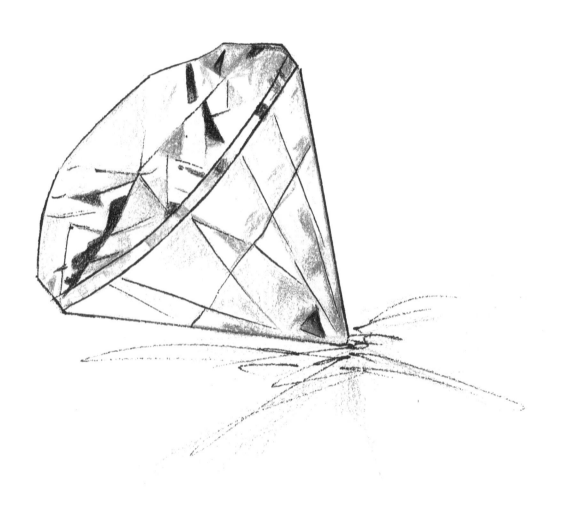

Diamonds go through a lot,
before you can see their true beauty.

To find a Diamonds beauty
you must look carefully
through sand,
rocks and remove layers
and layers of dirt.

It takes a lot, of digging Daddy said.

"DIGGING?" Tahi asked confused

"Yes, digging" Daddy said,

"but Pearls are formed inside Oysters".

Daddy showed Tahi a picture
of an Oyster

"How do they get inside Oysters".
Tahi asked,
struggling to say the word.

Tahi was now sitting up on Daddy's lap,
with a faraway look in her eye.

She now, also had a puzzled expression
on her face.

Tahi was, thinking,
'Daddy said, Diamonds come from rocks,
but Pearls come from Oysters'.

Daddy explained, that something
surprising happened with oysters.

"When an oyster gets upset, feels sad"

Or afraid it builds layers and layers of something called 'Nacre'.

Nacre becomes a Pearl!

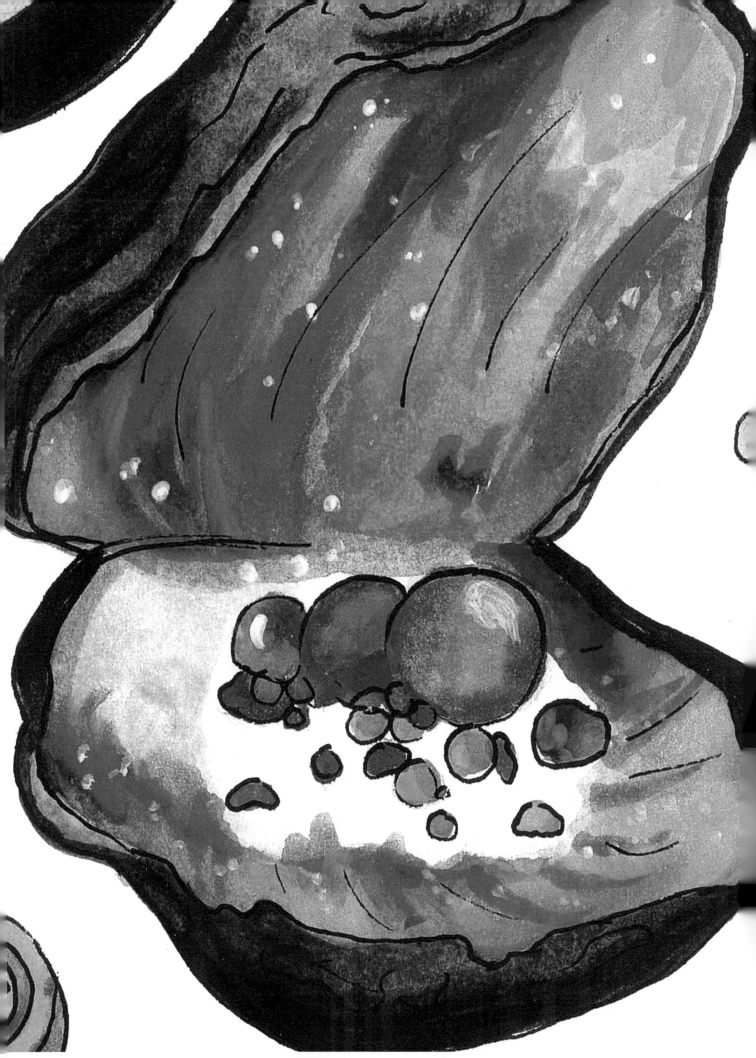

Pearls are the only gems that
come from nature
"That do not need anything"

"Nothing extra from us, me,or you for its beauty to be seen".

"Nothing?" Tahi asked.

"Nothing?" Daddy said.

"Daddy!" Tahi said "I don't want to be
a Diamond anymore"
"I'm beautiful just the way I am,
aren't I?"
"Because I am, a Pearl" "Yes you are"
Daddy said.

"Tomorrow you may find other Pearls in school too! Tahi leaped off Daddy's lap, her tears now forgotten.

She was now wondering, how many, Pearls she would find tomorrow."What would the Pearls look like?"
Tahi thought with excitement.

DADDY'S PEARL

SUBRENA JOSEPH is born in London of Grenadian, Carriacou heritage. She is the author of the book entitled ' TO WALK AROUND IT, TO MOVE IT OR TO LOVE IT' an autobiographical account of her life thus far.

Demonstrating her lived application of personal and transformational leadership to navigate life's challenges and barriers.

Subrena has lived experience of disability, living with dual physical disability diagnosis of Spina Bifida Culta and Chronic Inflammatory Demyelinating Polyneuropathy. When she was younger Subrena also wore a splint or foot brace very much like Tahi's.

Subrena has 20 plus years experience working in health and social care sector, specialising in the area of disability; within children's and adults social services, disability advocacy and as personal leadership speaker, mentor and life coach. - Subrena identifies as 'Proud Pearl'

stubsdisabilityservice@gmail.com
stubsdisabilitylife.co.uk

ALMASI SAMUELS is a Jamaican-born
Multidisciplinary Designer & Illustrator now
living in London.

She considers herself more of a traditional
artist when working, using watercolours,
acrylics, pen & ink.

Inspired by her Caribbean roots, her work aims
to evoke feelings of nostalgia, joyfulness &
positivity. By pairing her use of vibrant colours
and lines to create textures & details,

she creates illustrations that are child-like,
playful & wholesome.

The theme that runs throughout her work is
around healthy loving family relationships within
black culture that are not always depicted as
positive.

almasisamuels.com

Lightning Source UK Ltd.
Milton Keynes UK
UKHW051143031222
413232UK00002B/98